Happy
The Helping Horse

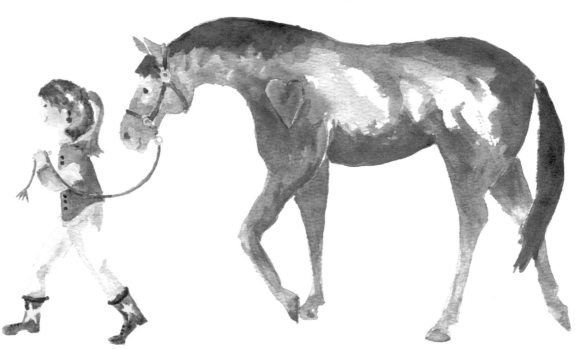

Written and Illustrated by Phyllis E. Gentry

Book design by Praise Saflor

Library of Congress Control Number: 2022903941

ISBN   979-8-9858408-0-3 (Paperback)

979-8-9858408-1-0 (Hardback)

979-8-9858408-2-7 (eBook)

To my sister, Sue,
who helped me find the right words
to tell the story of Happy the Helping Horse.

And to Happy,
one of the kindest horses I have ever known.

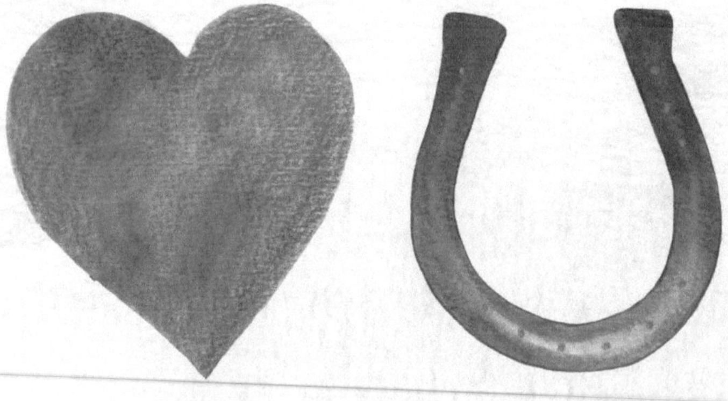

Introduction

Happy the Helping Horse is a true story. Happy is a real horse, and he has a condition called Equine Alopecia. This condition has caused him to lose most of his hair. Although several veterinarians have treated him, there is no cure.

Happy was a "discard horse" from a Show Barn because he had injured his back leg as a two year old. His owners did not think he was show material any longer. How lucky for me! I bought him, and he became a wonderful trail horse for me. Later, when he developed Equine Alopecia, he became a lesson horse for children and some adults, especially those with disabilities. His "Big Heart" has brought happiness to many people, and to me as well.

I wrote this book with the hope that it will touch the hearts of children and to anyone who loves horses as much as I do.

Alopecia
al.o.pe.ci.a
The partial or complete absence of hair from areas of the body where it normally grows; baldness.

Happy the Horse
was born one day,

On a beautiful farm
in a field of hay.

The sun was shining oh, so bright.

Birds were singing at the site.

Happy ran and
    played of course,
And he grew to be a shiny,
    black horse.

Happy was beautiful
    and kind from the start,
But most of all
    he had a Big Heart.

A very nice lady came
to visit one day,
And took him home
with her to stay.

The lady loved him
     right from the start,
And knew he was willing
     to give her his heart.

Together they rode
on a beautiful trail,

Laughing and singing
over hill and dale.

Soon they became
each other's best friend,

Galloping across
the fields like the wind.

But one day Happy
    did not want to play,
So the doctor came over.
    Was Happy okay?

Happy was sick
    and had lost so much hair,
He was afraid that all
    the children would stare.

The lady was kind
and patted his head,

And she told Happy
    there was nothing to dread.

Together they looked
for good things to do,

To keep him from feeling
so sad and so blue.

Now even though Happy
did not look the same,
Happy's Big Heart was
what gave him his name.

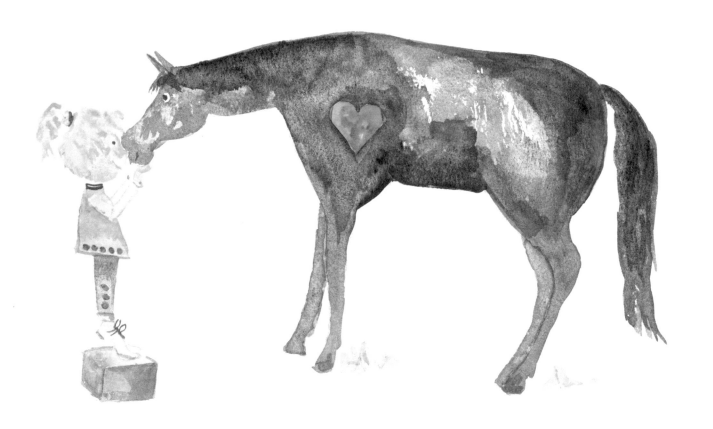

He knew it was much
    more important to care,
Than it was to worry
    about losing his hair.

He knew there were children
who had problems too,

And so Happy's love
    for these sweet children grew.

Happy was pleased
taking each for a ride.

Their faces all glowed
and he felt so much pride.

Sometimes Happy was their
first horse to ride,
With their Mama and Daddy
walking beside.

Happy helped them
    to laugh and to smile,
Fulfilling their hopes
    and dreams all the while.

The Helping Horse is
still Happy today,
And he and the children
together still play.

Happy learned a big lesson:
The more you give...
The happier life you
and others will live.

A few of my favorite quotes

"There is no better place to heal a broken heart than on the back of a horse."
   -Missy Lyons

"There is much we can learn from a friend who happens to be a horse."
   -Aleksandra Layland

"It's amazing what a healing effect horses can have on kids, particularly troubled kids, that might bridge the gap that a well intended human just can't do."
   -Buck Brannaman

"Put your hand on your horse and your heart in your hand."
   -Pat Parelli

"Give a horse what he needs, and he will give you his heart in return."
   -Anonymous

"Horses change lives. They give our young people confidence and self esteem. They provide peace and tranquility to troubled souls, they give us hope."
   -Toni Robinson

"A great horse will change your life. The truly special ones define it."
   -Anonymous

"No hour of life is wasted that is spent in the saddle."
   -Winston Churchill

"For one to fly, one needs only to take the reins."
   -Melissa James

"Don't judge a horse by his color, but instead, look for a horse with a good heart."
   -Anonymous

Made in United States
Troutdale, OR
12/07/2023

15419967R00021